Make your own!

Write in the first letter to make your own rhy
Draw a picture of your word. The Letterlander

Rhyme

Explain that words that sound the same at the end are words that rhyme.

Rhyming pairs

Join the words to the pictures to form rhyming pairs.

red

ball

small

cat

fat

bed

Listen

As you read the words together, encourage your child to listen to the way they sound alike at the end. Explain that this makes them into rhyming words.

Draw the rhymes

Draw a picture of...

...a fox in a box.

...a cat on a mat.

Volume

Say the sentences together several times. Have some fun and make a game of saying the rhyming words louder than the rest of the sentence.

Cross it out

Cross out the words that do not rhyme.

house

mouse

cake

locket

jelly

rocket

nest

hat

rat

clock

sock

cow

Point

Help strengthen the sound/symbol link by pointing to each word as you read them to your child. Help with the discovery that, except for the first letter or two, the rhyming words on this page both sound and **look** similar.

Tick it off

Tick the words that rhyme with 'tree'.

bee ☐

duck ☐

3

three ☐

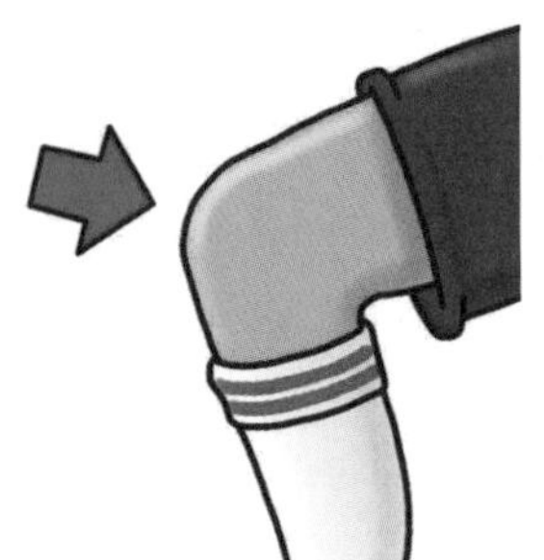

knee ☐

apple ☐

flower ☐

horse ☐

key ☐

Look

Help with the discovery that sometimes the rhyming part of the word will not look the same, but it will still **sound** the same.

Rhyming words

☐ cake

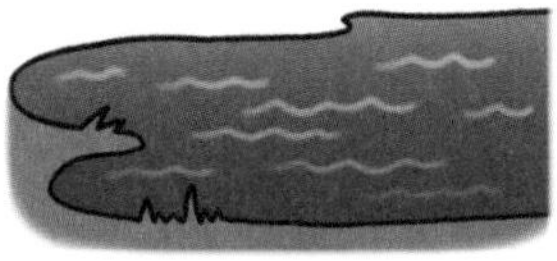

☐ lake

☐ snake

☐ rake

Look! I've got lots more rhyming words for you.

☐ whale

☐ nail

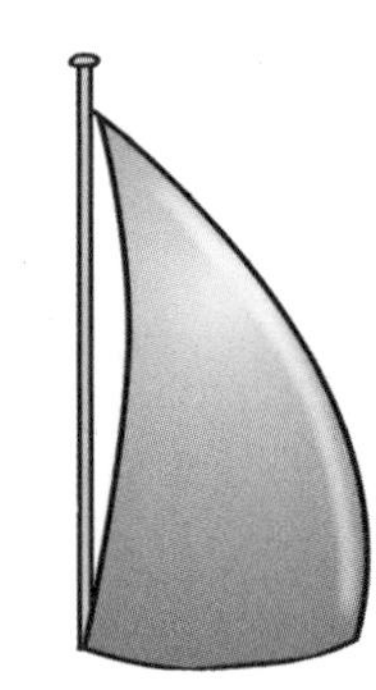

☐ sail

☐ snail

Look

Tick the words as you find the objects in the picture. Then colour the picture.

More matching words

Draw lines between the pictures to join the rhyming words.

book

pear

bear

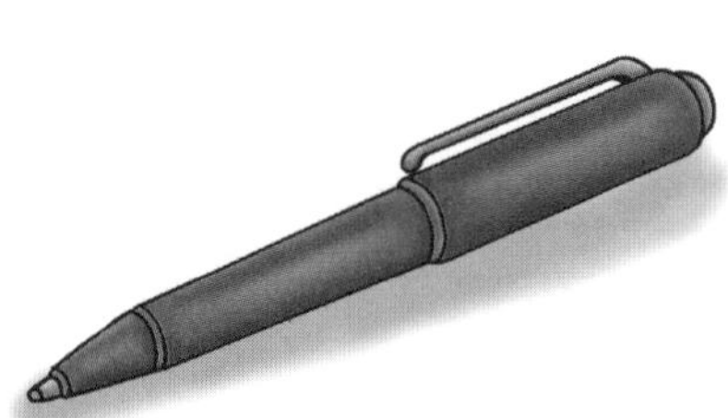

pen

hen

hook

Follow up this activity by asking your child to think of another rhyming word for each pair shown here, (e.g. ten, wear, look).

Letterland rhymes

Draw things that rhyme with the end of these Letterlanders' names.

Names

All of the Letterland character names are on the inside back cover if you need a reminder. Try drawing things that rhyme with other Letterland characters too.

Complete the poems

Write in the missing words to complete these poems.

Bouncy Ben has lots of fun
playing baseball in the sun.

But he should copy Clever Cat
and wear a lovely, shady _ _ _ .

Vicky Violet's in her van.
She's going to visit Yo-yo Man.
They're having tea with Sammy Snake
who's made a yummy chocolate _ _ _ _ .

The Letterland name game

Circle the pictures that rhyme with the Letterlanders' names.

gate

curl

bike

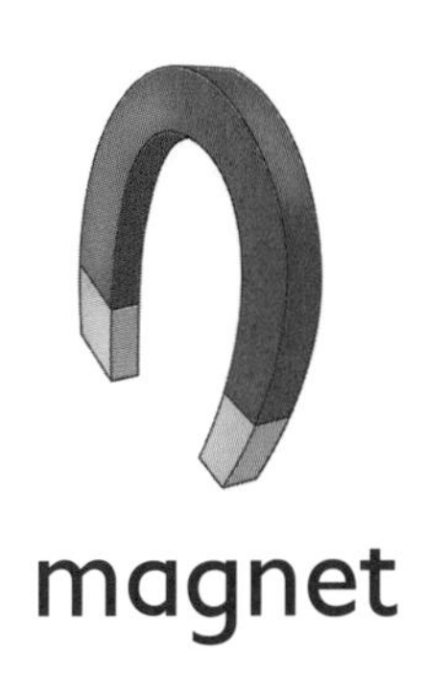

magnet

stick

nest

sun

rake

Letterland rhyming pairs

ring

bike

cake

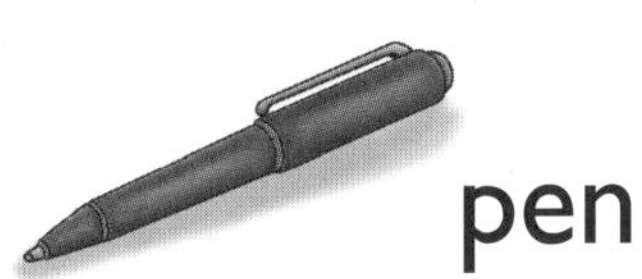

pen

truck

bed

Read the poems and try to fill in the missing rhymng word at the end of each one.

Annie Apple

Annie Apple is in her tree,
How many animals can she see?
Five pink piglets in their pen, and
five white lambs, that makes ___!

ten axe
fun ant

Bouncy Ben

Bouncy Ben is riding
on his bright, blue bike.
He's going up a mountain
to visit Munching ____!

Mum Mike
kite hike

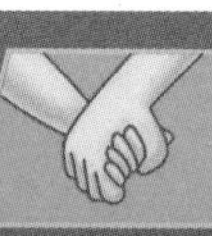

Point It's important to try and help your child realise that every spoken word can be written down and 'kept' on a page. This is why pointing to each word is useful.

Clever Cat

Clever Cat is playing.
She's dressed up as a clown.
She jumps into her car,
and drives around the ____!

moon hill
town cows

Dippy Duck

Here is the band from Letterland.
Down the road they come.
Look! Dippy Duck is at the front
banging on her ____!

door drum
desk pad

Eddy Elephant

Eddy loves to exercise.
He likes to stand on his head.
But sometimes he prefers to do
eleven push-ups _______!

shed in town
down instead

Enjoy

Research has shown that learning to love reading is one of the most important factors in success at school. So have a good time reading together!

Firefighter Fred

Firefighter Fred is going to work.
He's wearing his fireproof suit.
But what will he wear on his feet?
There's a frog inside his ____!

tooth shoe
food boot

Golden Girl

Round and round the garden,
her go-cart rushes past.
Slow down, Golden Girl, slow down.
You're going much too ____!

quick far
last fast

Harry Hat Man

Harry Hat Man likes to go
and visit his friends for tea.
"I like to look at their houses.
They're all so different, you ___!"

see tree
bee feet

Praise

Give lots of praise for 'reading' part or even the whole poem without your help!

Impy Ink

Impy Ink's invention is
an amazing breakfast robot.
It makes your toast, boils your egg,
and gives you your tea in a ___!

mop hot
pot bottle

Jumping Jim

Jumping Jim wants a drink.
He takes out his stripy jug,
and pours the tasty fruit juice,
into his nice new ___!

tub slug
pocket mug

Kicking King

Kicking King loves to kick
his football way up high.
But he prefers, on windy days,
to fly his kite in the ____!

sky wind
mud rain

Together

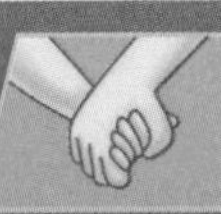

Read each poem slowly 2 or 3 times, and point to the words.
Then say, "You say it with me this time."

Lucy Lamp Light

Look out, Lucy Lamp Light!
You've let your basket spill.
Now all your lovely lemons
are rolling down the ____!

stairs mill
hill rock

Munching Mike

Munching Mike is hungry!
What would he like to eat?
Mushrooms and marshmallows
will make a tasty _____!

map dinner
treat seat

Noisy Nick

Noisy Nick is nibbling
nineteen nuts - crunch, crunch.
Never has Nick nibbled
nicer nuts for _____!

crunch bunch
supper lunch

Point

Guide the child's hand and first finger, pointing to the words while you say them together.

Oscar Orange

Oscar Orange is in the office.
There's nobody else in there.
Oscar pretends that he's the boss
and sits in the comfy ____!

pillow stairs
bed chair

Peter Puppy

Peter Puppy is in the park.
He's playing on the swing.
Flying high right through the air
is such a wonderful _____!

pond game
ring thing

Quarrelsome Queen

Quarrelsome Queen writes
her letters with a quill.
She must be very careful
that the ink does not _____!

drip fill
spill sting

Choose

As you read more poems, let your child choose one or two of the earlier poems they like most to read again.

Red Robot

Red Robot often takes things,
and puts them in his sack.
If you ever see him stealing, shout:
"Red Robot, put that ____!"

away down
back pack

Sammy Snake

Sammy Snake sometimes goes
for a snooze in the sun.
But a swim in the sea
is sssso much more ___!

fun bun
run sun

Talking Tess

Talking Tess's toothbrush
keeps her teeth all clean.
They really are the cleanest teeth
that you have ever ____!

green been
seem seen

Timing

Remember to choose a time to sit together to read these poems when there is nothing your child would rather be doing.

Uppy Umbrella

Up, up she goes, up, up in the sky,
right over the mountain top.
Uppy Umbrella flies so high,
we wonder when she will ____!

hop stop
fly jump

Vicky Violet

Vicky grows fresh vegetables.
She says, "I'll bet you know.
They're full of healthy vitamins
that help to make you ____!"

jump glow
trip grow

Walter Walrus

Whoosh! The wind blows hard
and makes the waves leap high.
Wheee! Watch Walter Walrus
splashing and whizzing __!

try away
by splash

Listen

Remember to give lots of praise for 'reading' part or even the whole poem without your help.

Fix-it Max

If you have some broken toys,
or a puncture in your ball,
we know who can mend the lot.
Give Fix-it Max a ____!

call tall
fall ball

Yellow Yo-yo Man

Yo-yo Man is fast asleep.
He doesn't hear the bell.
Shall we try to wake him up?
We think we'll have to ____!

shout try
yell spell

Zig Zag Zebra

Zig Zag and Zoe are having a race.
They whizz like the wind, whiz, whizzy!
With all those stripes zoom-zooming by,
they make us feel quite _____!

funny fizzy
fuzzy dizzy

Listen

Now you have finished an alphabet of poems go back and choose one or two favourites to read again.

Word families

How many words can you make with these endings?

bat

at

dig

ig

Listen

Help your child to write the words: **bat**, **cat**, **fat**, **mat**, **pat**; **dig**, **big**, **pig**, **fig**, **wig**.
Say each letter sound together as he or she writes it. This will strengthen the sound/symbol link.

Clever Cat & Harry Hat Man

Sometimes Clever Cat and Harry Hat Man do not make their usual sounds in words. This happens when Clever Cat sits next to the Hat Man and his hairy hat makes her nose tickle. Then all you can hear is her quietly sneezing, 'ch...'!

Rhyme

Clever Cat and Harry Hat Man have their own rhyme.

The Cat belongs to the Hat Man.
He lets her go where she pleases.
But when she sits down beside him,
she almost always sneezes!
"Ch! ch! ch!"

Have fun acting out the '**ch** story' together. Make sure the sneeze sounds like 'ch' and not 'ah-choo'!
There are many more clever rhymes to discover and also sing on the **Letterland Blends & Digraphs CD.**